# PASSWORD

## ENGLISH

# Skills Book

## 2b

### ACTIVITIES FOR GROUP WORK

Ginn

# Contents

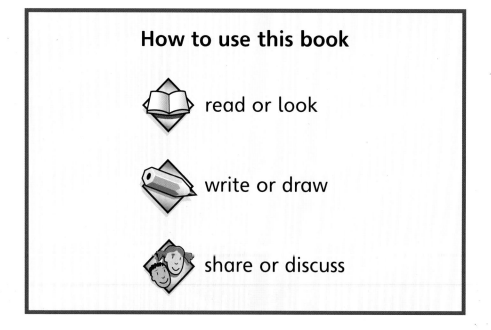

## How to use this book

read or look

write or draw

share or discuss

# Toy cupboard

Look at the toy cupboard.

Write the words.

**Vowel phonemes 2** ◆

**Skill:** Spelling words containing the phoneme *or*.
**Instructions:** Look at the items in the picture and write a list of all the words.
Remember that they all have the sound *or* but may be spelt in different ways.

# Making words

1. Look at these words.

2. Add *er* to each word like this:   jump + er = jumper

farm

play

sing

teach

paint

stick

3. Write three sentences using these words.

**Vowel phonemes 2** ◆◆
**Skill:** Spelling words containing the phoneme *er*.
**Instructions:** Add *er* to each of the words, then choose at least three of the words and use them in sentences.

# Philip the dolphin

1. Look at this newspaper.

**Daily NEWS**

**MEET PHILIP!**
The first dolphin to go to school

2. You are going to interview Philip on television. What questions will you ask him?

3. You could use these words to start your questions.

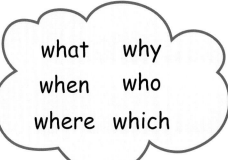

what    why
when    who
where   which

Consonant digraphs ◆◆◆
**Skill:** Using the consonant digraphs *ph* and *wh*.
**Instructions:** Think of questions to ask Philip the dolphin in a television interview.
Remember to use words with *wh* and *ph* and spell them carefully!

# Two words in one

1. Read this sentence.

   There is a pile of firewood
   beside the fireplace.

2. Write a sentence for these pictures.
   Use two compound words for each.

Compound words ♦♦

**Skill:** Spelling compound words correctly.
**Instructions:** Look carefully at each picture and write a sentence to go with it.
Use two compound words in each sentence.

# Count the syllables

1.  Read this poem.

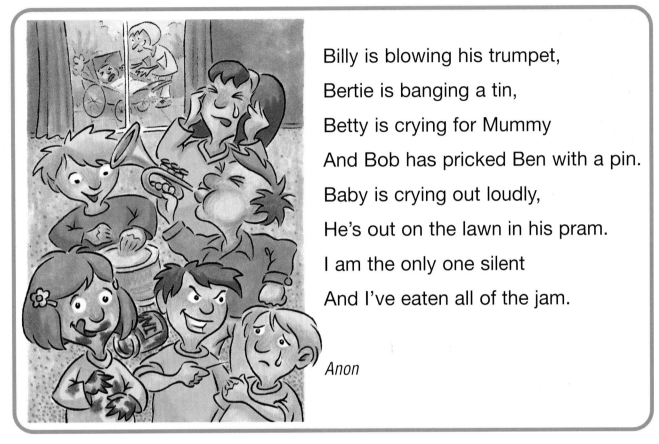

Billy is blowing his trumpet,

Bertie is banging a tin,

Betty is crying for Mummy

And Bob has pricked Ben with a pin.

Baby is crying out loudly,

He's out on the lawn in his pram.

I am the only one silent

And I've eaten all of the jam.

*Anon*

2. Write the words in two lists.

one syllable

two syllables

**Syllables** ◆◆
**Skill:** Identifying syllables in words.
**Instructions:** Read the poem and then write the words in two lists: ten words from the poem
that have one syllable, and ten words that have two syllables.

# Playtime prefixes

1. Read about the trouble at playtime.

What a bad playtime!
Some of you have been climbing the unsafe fence. It's lucky you were unhurt. Did you have to disobey Mrs Gordon? Now two footballs have disappeared. Why do you all disagree so much? Why are you so unkind to each other? It's unfair to behave like this - you know how much I dislike it.

2. Write the words in two lists.

un

dis

8

**Skill:** Identifying and spelling words with prefixes.
**Instructions:** Read the teacher's speech bubble carefully, then find the words beginning with *un* and *dis* and write them in two lists. If time, add some more words to each list.

# Clown opposites

 Look.

 Write the opposite words.

**Antonyms** ◆

**Skill:** Writing simple words to describe opposites.
**Instructions:** Look closely at the clowns. Discuss in your group, what opposites you can see?
Write simple pairs of words to show opposites, e.g. *tall-short*.

# At the shops

 1. Look at the pictures. Sam and Pam are going to the shops with their Mum.

**1**

**2**

**3**

**4**

**5**

**6**

 2. Write a sentence for each picture.

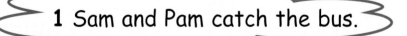
**1** Sam and Pam catch the bus.

 3. Read each sentence.
Does it make sense?

Accuracy and agreement ◆ ◆

**Skill:** Writing sentences with grammatical sense and accuracy.
**Instructions:** Look carefully at the pictures, then write a sentence to go with each picture. As a group, read each sentence and decide whether each one makes sense, or not. Do any of the sentences need to be changed?

# Yesterday

1. Ali's class did PE yesterday. Look at the pictures.

hop

catch

throw

skip

run

sit

2. Write a sentence for each picture.
   Start each sentence with 'Yesterday'.

Yesterday Ali hopped on one leg.

**Verb tenses** ◆ ◆
**Skill:** Writing sentences in past tense.
**Instructions:** Look at the pictures and write sentences describing what Ali did,
starting each sentence with 'Yesterday'.

# Having a bad day!

1. Look at the pictures.

2. Write what happened on Ali's bad day.

I had a bad day yesterday. On the way to school . . .

Verb tenses ✦✦

**Skill:** Writing a narrative passage using past tense.
**Instructions:** Look closely at the pictures and imagine yourself as the boy. Using the opening given, write the story of what happened in your bad day, using the past tense.

# Alex's bad mood

1.  Read this story.

"Oh good," said Alex's mother. "That's Roy come to play."

"It's no good," said Alex. "I don't want to play with Roy."

And he stomped off into his bedroom.

Alex's mother opened the door. It was Roy with his big sister Renee.

"Sorry I can't stop," said Renee.

"Dad's waiting in the car. I don't want to be late at the hairdresser's."

"Come in, Roy," said Alex's mother. "Alex will be here in a minute."

She said it very loudly, hoping Alex would hear.

*Mary Dickinson*

2. Write what the characters say in speech bubbles.

> Use CAPITALS and **bold letters** for emphasis.

13

**Speech marks** ◆◆◆

**Skill:** Exploring different ways of presenting speech.
**Instructions:** Read the extract carefully, then rewrite it using speech bubbles. If possible, use capitals and bold letters to emphasise the text.

# Tigger's walk

 1. Follow the arrows to see where Tigger the cat went.

through
the gate

over the
bridge

around
the pond

through
the trees

across the
flowers

under the
fence

2. Write one sentence about where Tigger went.

**Commas in lists** ◆◆

**Skill:** Writing a list sentence with commas.
**Instructions:** Look at the map showing where Tigger went on his walk. Using the labels,
write one sentence where Tigger went, using commas.

# Freeze-frame moments

1. Choose a picture.

Baby Bear looked at his bed and saw Goldilocks fast asleep under the covers.

The second ugly sister tried to put on the glass slipper. She pushed and pushed, but no matter how hard she tried, the slipper would not fit.

2. Practise a freeze-frame.

3. Role-play what happens next.

**Traditional stories** ◆ ◆

**Skill:** Using freeze framing to help retell traditional story.
**Instructions:** Look at the two pictures and read the text. In groups of two or three, freeze-frame one of the scenes, taking account of the characters, their feelings and expressions. Then continue an improvised role-play from this scene.

# Tropical beach

 1. Look at the beach setting from *Gregory Cool*.

 2. Write words to describe this setting.

3. Write a story using this setting and your words.

 Settings ◆◆

**Skill:** Using a story setting to write a different story.
**Instructions:** Look at the setting in the picture, and think up words and phrases to describe it.
Use these to help you write a story set at this beach.

# Don't do that!

1. Read this poem.

**Don't**

Don't do,

Don't do, Don't do that.

Don't pull faces,

Don't tease the cat.

Don't pick your ears,

Don't be rude at school.

Who do they think I am?

Some kind of fool?

One day

They'll say

Don't put toffee in my coffee

don't pour gravy on the baby

don't put beer in his ear

don't stick your toes up his nose.

*Michael Rosen*

 2. Read the last four lines.

 3. Make a list of rhyming pairs of words.

 4. Write some more lines using your rhyming pairs.

Don't put bread on your head.
Don't put kippers in my slippers.

Poetry patterns ◆◆◆

**Skill:** Writing lines to follow a poetry pattern.
**Instructions:** Read the poem *Don't*, and make up new lines based on the pattern of the last four lines of the poem. Some new lines are given to help.

# Counting sheep

1. Read the poem.

**Counting sheep**

They said,
"If you can't get to sleep
try counting sheep."
I tried.
It didn't work.

They said,
"Still awake? Count rabbits, dogs,
leaping frogs."
I tried.
It didn't work.

They said,
"It's very late. Count rats,
or red-eyed bats!"
I tried.
It didn't work.

They said,
"Stop counting stupid sheep!"
EYES CLOSED! DON'T PEEP!
I tried
and fell asleep.

*Wes Magee*

 2. Write the answers to the questions.

**a.** Who is the poet?

**b.** How many verses are there in the poem?

**c.** What does the child in the poem want to do?

**d.** What did the child stop doing in verse 4?

**e.** Why do you think 'EYES CLOSED! DON'T PEEP!'
is written in capital letters?

**f.** Write the words in the poem that rhyme.

Favourite poems and poets ♦♦♦
**Skill:** Answering comprehension questions about a favourite poem.
**Instructions:** Read the poem and answer the comprehension questions on a sheet of paper.

# Dictionary search

Choose a dictionary.

Find and write.

1. the first word in **c**

2. the last word in **h**

3. the last word in **b**

4. the word after **cat**

5. the definition of **snow**

6. the definition of **cat**

7. the word before **house**

**Alphabetically ordered texts** ◆◆
**Skill:** Looking up initial letters, words and definitions in a dictionary.
**Instructions:** Choose a dictionary from the class collection, and look up the different things listed, writing your answers on a piece of paper.

# Making a glossary

Write in alphabetical order.

pass

goal

kick

corner

penalty

foul

halftime

goalkeeper

dribble

**Alphabetically ordered texts**

**Skill:** Ordering glossary entries correctly.
**Instructions:** Look at the football words and write them in alphabetical order.
If time, write simple definitions for the first few words.

# Drawing a picture

1. Read the flow chart for drawing a picture.

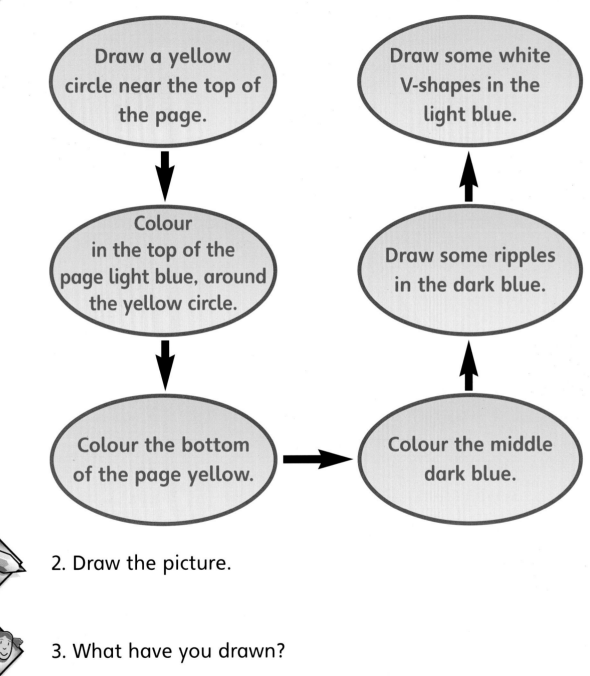

Draw a yellow circle near the top of the page.

Colour in the top of the page light blue, around the yellow circle.

Colour the bottom of the page yellow.

Colour the middle dark blue.

Draw some ripples in the dark blue.

Draw some white V-shapes in the light blue.

2. Draw the picture.

3. What have you drawn?

**Explanations** ◆◆

**Skill:** Reading and responding to a flow diagram.
**Instructions:** Using crayons or coloured pencils, follow the flow diagram to draw a picture.
Write what you think you have drawn underneath the picture.

# The year of an oak tree

 1. Read the information and look at the pictures.

**Spring**
The oak tree grows new green shoots.

**Summer**
The green shoots grow into beautiful green leaves. Acorns grow.

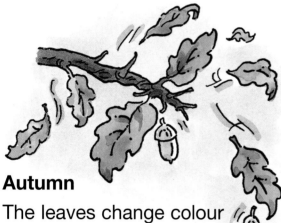

**Autumn**
The leaves change colour and then fall to the ground. The acorns fall off and some grow into oak trees.

**Winter**
The oak tree rests. Its branches are bare.

 2. Draw a life cycle diagram of an oak tree.

Explanations ◆◆◆

**Skill:** Making a cyclical diagram to help explain a process.
**Instructions:** Look at the sentences and pictures carefully. Draw a simple cyclical diagram with arrows, illustrations and important information.